Oh, I like his way of talking,
    Yes, I do.
It's the nicest way of talking
    Just for two.
And a Help-yourself with Rabbit
    Though it may become a habit,
Is a *pleasant* sort of habit
    For a Pooh.

"That's right," said Eeyore. "Sing. Umty-tiddly, umty-too. Here we go gathering Nuts and May. Enjoy yourself."

"I am," said Pooh.

"You seem so sad, Eeyore."

"Sad? Why should I be sad? It's my birthday. The happiest day of the year."

"Oh! Well, many happy returns of the day, Eeyore."

"And many happy returns to you, Pooh Bear."

"But it isn't *my* birthday."

"No, it's mine."

"But you said 'Many happy returns'—"

"Well, why not? You don't always want to be miserable on my birthday, do you?"

"It's bad enough," said Eeyore, almost breaking down, "being miserable myself, what with no presents and no cake and no candles, and no proper notice taken of me at all, but if everybody else is going to be miserable too —"

This was too much for Pooh. "Stay there!" he called to Eeyore, as he turned and hurried back home as quick as he could; for he felt that he must get poor Eeyore a present of *some* sort at once, and he could always think of a proper one afterwards.

The first thing Pooh did was to go to the cupboard to see if he had quite a small jar of honey left; and he had, so he took it down.

"I'm giving this to Eeyore," he explained, "as a present. What are *you* going to give?"

So off Piglet trotted; and in the other direction went Pooh, with his jar of honey.

It was a warm day, and he had a long way to go. He hadn't gone more than half-way when a sort of funny feeling began to creep all over him . . . It was just as if somebody inside him were saying, "Now then, Pooh, time for a little something."

"Dear, dear," said Pooh, "I didn't know it was as late as that." So he sat down and took the top off his jar of honey. "Lucky I brought this with me," he thought.

And then, suddenly, he remembered. He had eaten
Eeyore's birthday present!

"*Bother!*" said Pooh.

"What *shall* I do? I *must* give him *something*."

"Many happy returns of Eeyore's birthday," said Pooh.

"Oh, is that what it is?"

"What are you giving him, Owl?"

"What are *you* giving him, Pooh?"

"I'm giving him a Useful Pot to Keep Things In. . ."

"Somebody has been keeping honey in it," said Owl.

Well, he washed the pot out, and dried it,
while Owl licked the end of his pencil,
and wondered how to spell 'birthday'.

HIPY PAPY BTHUTHDTH THUTHDA
BTHUTHDY

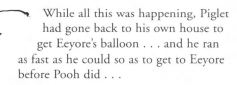

While all this was happening, Piglet had gone back to his own house to get Eeyore's balloon . . . and he ran as fast as he could so as to get to Eeyore before Pooh did . . .

BANG!!!???***!!!

"Thank you, Piglet," said Eeyore. "You don't mind my asking," he went on, "but what colour was this balloon when it – when it *was* a balloon?"

"It's a Useful Pot," said Pooh. "Here it is. And it's got 'A Very Happy Birthday with love from Pooh' written on it."

. . . Eeyore picked the balloon up with his teeth, and placed it carefully in the pot; picked it out and put it on the ground; and then picked it up again and put it carefully back.

"Piglet, I have decided something."

"What have you decided, Pooh?"

"I have decided to catch a Heffalump."

Where should they dig the Very Deep Pit?

Piglet said that the best place would
be somewhere where a Heffalump
was, just before he fell into it, only
about a foot further on.

"Suppose," he said to Piglet, "*you* wanted to catch *me*, how would you do it?"

"Well," said Piglet, ". . . I should make a Trap, and I should put a Jar of Honey in the Trap, and you would smell it, and you would go in after it . . ."

So Piglet put the jar at the bottom of the Pit, and climbed out, and they went off home together.

The more he tried to sleep, the more he couldn't. He tried Counting Sheep . . . and, as that was no good, he tried counting Heffalumps . . . For some minutes he lay there miserably, but when the five hundred and eighty-seventh Heffalump was licking its jaws, and saying to itself, "Very good honey this, I don't know when I've tasted better," Pooh could bear it no longer.

. . . there was a little left at the very bottom of the jar, and he pushed his head right in . . .

By and by Piglet woke up . . .
What was a Heffalump like? . . .
Was it Fond of Pigs at all?
If it was Fond of Pigs, did it make
any difference *what sort of Pig?*

So off he went. At first he thought that there wouldn't be a Heffalump in the Trap, and then he thought that there would, and as he got nearer he was *sure* that there would, because he could hear it heffalumping about it like anything.

And all the time Winnie-the-Pooh had been trying to get the honey-jar off his head. The more he shook it, the more tightly it stuck.

So at last he lifted up his head, jar and all, and made a loud, roaring noise . . .

"Help, help!" cried Piglet, "a Heffalump, a Horrible Heffalump!" and he scampered off as hard as he could, still crying out, "Help, help, a Herrible Hoffalump! Hoff, Hoff, a Hellible Horralump! Holl, Holl, a Hoffable Hellerump!"

"What did it look like?"

"Like – like — It had the biggest head you ever saw,
Christopher Robin. A great enormous thing, like – like
nothing. A huge big – well, like a – I don't know – like
an enormous big nothing. Like a jar."

Suddenly Christopher Robin began to laugh . . . and –
Crash went the Heffalump's head against the tree-root,
Smash went the jar, and out came Pooh's head again . . .

Piglet

Tra-la-la, tra-la-la, as he stretched
up as high as he could go, and
then *Tra-la-la, tra-la – oh,
help! – la*, as he tried to reach
his toes.

"Aha!" said Pooh. (*Rum-tum-tiddle-um-tum.*) "If I know anything about anything, that hole means Rabbit," he said, "and Rabbit means Company," he said, "and Company means Food and Listening-to-Me-Humming and such like. *Rum-tum-tum-tiddle-um.*"

. . . when Rabbit said, "Honey or condensed milk with your bread?" he was so excited that he said, "Both," and then, so as not to seem greedy, he added, "But don't bother about the bread, please." And for a long time after that he said nothing . . . until at last, humming to himself in a rather sticky voice, he got up, shook Rabbit lovingly by the paw, and said that he must be going on.

Now, by this time Rabbit wanted to go for a walk too, and finding the front door full, he went out by the back door, and came round to Pooh, and looked at him.

"It all comes," said Pooh crossly, "of not having front doors big enough."

"It all comes," said Rabbit sternly, "of eating too much. I thought at the time," said Rabbit, "only I didn't like to say anything," said Rabbit, "that one of us was eating too much," said Rabbit, "and I knew it wasn't *me*," he said.

Christopher
Robin lived at
the other end
of the Forest,
and when he
came back
with Rabbit,
and saw the
front half of
Pooh, he said,
"Silly old
Bear," in such
a loving voice
that everybody
felt quite
hopeful again.

"I'm afraid no meals," said Christopher Robin,
"because of getting thin quicker. But we *will* read to you."
Bear began to sigh, and
then found he couldn't
because he was so tightly
stuck; and a tear rolled
down his eye, as he said:
"Then would you read
a Sustaining Book, such
as would help and
comfort a Wedged Bear
in Great Tightness?"

So he took hold of
Pooh's front paws
and Rabbit took
hold of
Christopher Robin,
and all Rabbit's
friends and relations
took hold of Rabbit,
and they all pulled
together . . .

And for a long time
Pooh only said,
"*Ow!*" . . .
And "*Oh!*" . . .
And then, all of a
sudden, he said
"*Pop!*" just as if a
cork were coming
out of a bottle.

. . . there was a wooden bridge, almost as broad as a road, with wooden rails on each side of it. Christopher Robin could just get his chin on to the top rail, if he wanted to, but it was more fun to stand on the bottom rail, so that he could lean right over, and watch the river slipping slowly away beneath him.

He had just come to
the bridge; and not
looking where he was
going, he tripped
over something, and
the fir-cone jerked
out of his paw into
the river.

"That's funny," said Pooh. "I dropped it on the other side," said Pooh, "and it came out on this side! I wonder if it would do it again?" And he went back for some more fir-cones.

Then he dropped two in at once, and leant over the bridge to see which of them would come out first; and one of them did; but as they were both the same size, he didn't know if it was the one which he wanted to win, or the other one.

And that was the beginning of the game called Poohsticks, which Pooh invented, and which he and his friends used to play on the edge of the Forest. But they played with sticks instead of fir-cones, because they were easier to mark.

Now one day Pooh and Piglet and Rabbit and Roo were all playing Poohsticks together. They had dropped their sticks in when Rabbit said "Go!" and then they had hurried across to the other side of the bridge, and now they were all leaning over the edge, waiting to see whose stick would come out first. But it was a long time coming, because the river was very lazy that day, and hardly seemed to mind if it didn't ever get there at all.

"I can see mine!" cried Roo. "No, I can't, it's something else. Can you see yours, Piglet? I thought I could see mine, but I couldn't. There it is! No, it isn't. Can you see yours, Pooh?"

Rabbit leant over further than ever, looking for his and Roo wriggled up and down, calling out "Come on, stick! Stick, stick, stick!" and Piglet got very excited because his was the only one which had been seen, and that meant that he was winning.

"Are you *sure* it's mine?" squeaked Piglet excitedly. "Yes, because it's grey. A big grey one. Here it comes! A very – big – grey — Oh, no, it isn't, it's Eeyore."

Looking very calm, very dignified, with his legs in the air, came Eeyore from beneath the bridge.

"But, Eeyore," said Pooh in distress, "what can we – I mean, how shall we – do you think if we —"

"Yes," said Eeyore. "One of those would be just the thing. Thank you, Pooh."

Pooh dropped his stone. There was a loud splash, and
Eeyore disappeared . . .
And then . . . something grey showed for a moment by
the river bank . . . and it got slowly bigger and bigger . . .
and at last it was Eeyore coming out.

"How did you
fall in, Eeyore?"
asked Rabbit, as
he dried him
with Piglet's
handkerchief.

"I was
BOUNCED,"
said Eeyore.

"I didn't really. I had a cough, and I happened to be behind Eeyore, and I said, '*Grrrr-oppp-ptschschschz.*'"

"Well, I sort of boffed," said Tigger.

"Hush!" said Rabbit, holding up his paw. "What does Christopher Robin think about it all? That's the point."

"Well," said Christopher Robin, not quite sure what it was all about. "*I* think —"

"*I* think we all ought to play Poohsticks."

So they did. And Eeyore, who had never played it before, won more times than anybody else; and Roo fell in twice, the first time by accident and the second time on purpose, because he suddenly saw Kanga coming from the Forest, and he knew he'd have to go to bed anyhow.

. . . and Tigger and Eeyore went off together, because Eeyore wanted to tell Tigger How to Win at Poohsticks, which you do by letting your stick drop in a twitchy sort of way, if you understand what I mean, Tigger; and Christopher Robin and Pooh and Piglet were left on the bridge by themselves.

One day when he was out walking, he came to an open place in the middle of the forest, and in the middle of this place was a large oak-tree, and, from the top of the tree, there came a loud buzzing-noise.

"If there's a buzzing-noise, somebody's making a buzzing-noise, and the only reason for making a buzzing-noise that *I* know of is because you're a bee."

Then he thought another long time, and said: "And the only reason for being a bee that I know of is making honey."

"And the only
reason for
making honey
is so as *I* can
eat it."

Isn't it funny
How a bear likes honey?
Buzz! Buzz! Buzz!
I wonder why he does?

It's a very funny thought that, if Bears were Bees,
They'd build their nests at the *bottom* of trees.
And that being so (if the Bees were Bears),
We shouldn't have to climb up all these stairs.

"It all comes, I suppose," he decided, as he said good-bye to the last branch, spun round three times, and flew gracefully into a gorse-bush, "it all comes of *liking* honey so much. Oh, help!"

"What do you want a balloon for?" you said. Winnie-the-Pooh looked round to see that nobody was listening, put his paw to his mouth, and said in a deep whisper: "*Honey!*"

Well, you both went out with the blue balloon . . .
and Winnie-the-Pooh went to a very muddy place
that he knew of, and rolled and rolled until he was
black all over . . .

"You look like a Bear holding on to a balloon," you said.

"Not," said Pooh anxiously, "— not like a small black cloud in a blue sky?"

" . . . Well, now, if you walk up and down with your umbrella, saying, 'Tut-tut, it looks like rain,' I shall do what I can by singing a little Cloud Song, such as a cloud might sing . . ."

How sweet to be a Cloud
    Floating in the Blue!
Every little cloud
Always sings aloud.

"How sweet to be a Cloud
    Floating in the Blue!"
It makes him very proud
To be a little cloud.

The bees were still buzzing as suspiciously as ever. Some of them, indeed, left their nests and flew all round the cloud as it began the second verse of this song, and one bee sat down on the nose of the cloud for a moment, and then got up again.

"I have just been thinking, and I have come to a very important decision. *These are the wrong sort of bees.*"

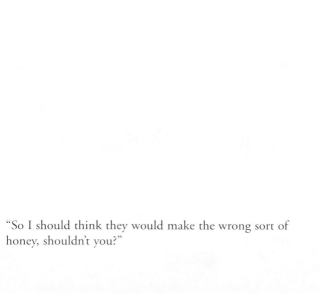

"So I should think they would make the wrong sort of honey, shouldn't you?"

"*Ow!*" said Pooh.

"Did I miss?" you asked.

"You didn't exactly *miss*," said Pooh, "but you missed the *balloon*."

. . . his arms were so stiff from holding on to the string of the balloon all that time that they stayed up straight in the air for more than a week, and whenever a fly came and settled on his nose he had to blow it off. And I think – but I am not sure – that *that* is why he was always called Pooh.

Cottleston, Cottleston, Cottleston Pie,
A fly can't bird, but a bird can fly.
Ask me a riddle and I reply:
"*Cottleston, Cottleston, Cottleston Pie.*"

That was the first verse. When he had finished it, Eeyore didn't actually say that he didn't like it, so Pooh very kindly sang the second verse to him:

Cottleston, Cottleston, Cottleston Pie,
A fish can't whistle and neither can I.
Ask me a riddle and I reply:
"Cottleston, Cottleston, Cottleston Pie."

Cottleston, Cottleston, Cottleston Pie,
Why does a chicken, I don't know why.
Ask me a riddle and I reply:
"Cottleston, Cottleston, Cottleston Pie."

COTTLESTON PIE

Pastry:
175 g (6 oz) butter or margarine
250 g (8 oz) self-raising flour
1 teaspoon salt
250 g (8 oz) cold, cooked mashed potato
1 tablespoon milk
1 beaten egg yolk

Filling:
1 large or 2 medium onions, chopped
125 g (4 oz) mushrooms, sliced
500 g (1 lb) mixed vegetables, either frozen or fresh,
  diced or sliced appropriately*
2 teaspoons mixed herbs
300 ml (½ pint) white sauce (see below)
125 g (4 oz) grated cheddar cheese
salt
pepper

White Sauce: makes ½ pint
15 g (½ oz) butter
15 g (½ oz) plain flour
300 ml (½ pint) milk
2 teaspoons Dijon mustard
salt
pepper

Dice and fry the onions in a little butter, adding the sliced mushrooms, mixed herbs, salt, pepper and other vegetables when the onions have become transparent. (Cook root vegetables separately in boiling water.) Remove the vegetables from the heat when they have become tender, and drain off the juices.

For the pastry: rub the butter or margarine into the flour, stir in the salt and work this mixture into the mashed potato. Then add the milk. Knead on a floured board until the dough is smooth and fairly soft. Roll out the pastry and use to line a large, shallow, ovenproof dish. Bake blind in a preheated oven at 200°C, 400°F, Gas Mark 6, for 20 minutes or until it is a light golden brown.

While the pastry is cooking, make the white sauce. Melt the butter in a small saucepan, taking care not to let it colour. Stir in the flour and cook for 1 minute, stirring continuously. Still stirring, add the milk. Continue to stir while bringing the mixture to the boil. Add the mustard, salt and pepper, and remove from the heat when the sauce has thickened.

Mix all the vegetables into the white sauce and season to taste. Remove the pastry from the oven, allow to cool a little, then fill with the vegetable mixture. Smooth the top, and sprinkle on the grated cheese. Brush the edges of the pastry with the beaten egg yolk and return to the oven for 30 minutes, or until the cheese has melted and is beginning to brown.

Serve hot. Makes about four portions.

* *A selection from the following could be chosen, or any other*
  favourites you may have:

broccoli	carrot	celery
courgette	leek	parsnip
red or green peppers	sweetcorn	tomatoes

"And how are you?" said Winnie-the-Pooh.
Eeyore shook his head from side to side.
"Not very how," he said. "I don't seem to
have felt at all how for a long time."

So Eeyore stood there, gazing sadly
at the ground, and Winnie-the-Pooh
walked all round him once.

"Why, what's happened to your tail?"
he said in surprise.

"Well, either a tail
is there or it isn't
there. You can't
make a mistake
about it, and yours
isn't there!"
"Then what is?"
"Nothing."

"That Accounts for a Good Deal," said Eeyore gloomily. "It Explains Everything. No Wonder."

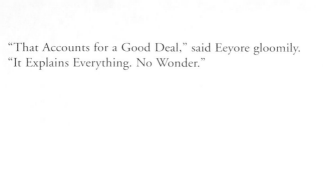

"You must have left it somewhere," said Winnie-the-Pooh. "Somebody must have taken it," said Eeyore. "How Like Them," he added, after a long silence.

"Eeyore," he said solemnly, "I, Winnie-the-Pooh, will find your tail for you."

"Thank you, Pooh," answered Eeyore. "You're a real friend," said he. "Not Like Some," he said.

So Winnie-the-Pooh went off to find Eeyore's tail.

Owl lived at The Chestnuts, an old-world residence of great charm, which was grander than anybody else's, or seemed so to Bear, because it had both a knocker *and* a bell-pull.

WOL

"Hallo, Pooh," he said. "How's things?"

"Terrible and Sad," said Pooh, "because Eeyore, who is a friend of mine, has lost his tail. And he's Moping about it. So could you very kindly tell me how to find it for him?"

"Well," said Owl, "the customary
procedure in such cases is as follows."
"What does Crustimoney Proceedcake
mean?" said Pooh. "For I am a Bear of Very
Little Brain, and long words Bother me."

CRUSTIMONEY PROCEEDCAKE

75 g (3 oz) butter or margarine
150 g (5 oz) caster sugar
2 drops of almond essence
50 g (2 oz) ground almonds
finely grated rind of ½ lemon
2 large eggs, beaten
125 g (4 oz) plain flour, sifted
15 g (½ oz) flaked almonds
2 teaspoons icing sugar, sifted

Beat the butter or margarine, caster sugar and almond essence
together until light and fluffy. Beat in the ground almonds and
lemon rind. Add the eggs a little at a time, beating well between
each addition, then fold in the flour. Turn into a greased and
floured 15 cm (6 inch) round cake tin, smooth the top and
sprinkle on the flaked almonds and icing sugar.

   Bake in a preheated moderate oven, 180°C (350°F), Gas Mark
4, for 45 to 50 minutes,* then test with a skewer to see if it is
cooked through. If necessary reduce the heat to 160°C, 325°F,
Gas Mark 3, and test every 5 minutes until the skewer comes out
clean. Leave in the tin for 5 minutes, then turn out and cool on a
wire rack.

** If using a fan assisted oven, follow the manufacturer's instructions for
adjusting the time and the temperature.*

"A lick of honey," murmured Bear to himself, "or – or not, as the case may be." And he gave a deep sigh, and tried very hard to listen to what Owl was saying.

But Owl went on and on, using longer and longer words, until at last he came back to where he started . . .

"Handsome bell-rope, isn't it?" said Owl.

Pooh nodded.

"It reminds me of something," he said, "but I can't think what. Where did you get it?"

"I just came across it in the Forest. It was hanging over a bush, and I thought at first somebody lived there, so I rang it, and nothing happened . . .

. . . and
then I
rang it
again very
loudly,
and it
came off
in my
hand, and
as nobody
seemed to
want it, I
took it
home,
and —"
"Owl,"
said Pooh
solemnly,
"you
made a
mistake.
Somebody
did want
it."

"Who?"
"Eeyore. My dear
friend Eeyore. He was
– he was fond of it."
"Fond of it?"
"Attached to it," said
Winnie-the-Pooh
sadly.

So with these words he
unhooked it, and carried it
back to Eeyore; and when
Christopher Robin had
nailed it on in its right
place again, Eeyore frisked
about the forest, waving his tail so
happily that Winnie-the-Pooh came over all funny, and
had to hurry home for a little snack of something to
sustain him.

What shall we do about poor little Tigger?
If he never eats nothing he'll never get bigger.
He doesn't like honey and haycorns and thistles
Because of the taste and because of the bristles.
And all the good things which an animal likes
Have the wrong sort of swallow or too many spikes.

But whatever his weight in pounds, shillings, and ounces,
He always seems bigger because of his bounces.

"Oh, there you are, Tigger!" said Christopher Robin. "I knew you'd be somewhere."

"I've been finding things in the Forest," said Tigger importantly. "I've found a pooh and a piglet and an eeyore, but I can't find any breakfast."

So they went into Kanga's house, and when Roo had said, "Hallo, Pooh," and "Hallo, Piglet," once, and "Hallo, Tigger," twice, because he had never said it before and it sounded funny . . .

. . . they told Kanga what they wanted, and Kanga said very kindly, "Well, look in my cupboard, Tigger dear, and see what you'd like."

"Shall I look, too?" said Pooh, who was beginning to feel a little eleven o'clockish.

And he found a small tin
of condensed milk, and
something seemed to tell
him that Tiggers didn't like
this, so he took it into a
corner by itself, and went
with it to see that nobody
interrupted it.

But the more Tigger put his nose into this and his paw into that, the more things he found which Tiggers didn't like.

. . . Kanga was saying, "Now, Roo dear, you remember what you promised."

"What is it?" whispered Tigger to Piglet.

"His Strengthening Medicine," said Piglet. "He hates it."

So Tigger came closer, and he leant over the back of Roo's chair, and suddenly he put out his tongue, and took one large golollop . . .

"He's taken my medicine, he's taken my medicine, he's taken my medicine!" sang Roo happily, thinking it was a tremendous joke.

. . . a peaceful smile
came over his face
as he said, "So *that's*
what Tiggers like!"

Which explains why he always lived at Kanga's house afterwards, and had Extract of Malt for breakfast, dinner, and tea. And sometimes, when Kanga thought he wanted strengthening, he had a spoonful or two of Roo's breakfast after meals as medicine.

MALTED TEA BREAD

300 ml (½ pint) warm water
1 teaspoon sugar
1 tablespoon dried yeast
500 g (1 lb) plain flour
1 teaspoon salt
75 g (3 oz) malt extract
50 g (2 oz) black treacle
25 g (1 oz) butter or margarine
250 g (8 oz) sultanas
clear honey, to glaze

Measure the water into a jug. Sprinkle over the sugar and yeast
and leave for about 10 minutes until frothy. Place the flour and salt
in a mixing bowl. Place the malt extract, treacle and butter or
margarine in a pan and heat gently until the fat has melted. Then
make a well in the centre of the flour and pour in the warmed malt
mixture, the yeast liquid and the sultanas. Beat well to form a
smooth batter. Divide the mixture between 2 greased 500g (1lb)
loaf tins and place in a large, oiled polythene bag. Leave to rise for
about 1 hour, until the mixture is almost to the top of the tins.

Bake in a preheated oven, 200°C, 400°F, Gas Mark 6 for 50
minutes* until firm to touch. Turn out and cool on a wire rack.
Brush with honey while still warm.

* If using a fan assisted oven, follow the manufacturer's instructions for
  adjusting the time and the temperature.

Christopher Robin was sitting outside his door, putting on his Big Boots. As soon as he saw the Big Boots, Pooh knew that an Adventure was going to happen . . .

"Do you think you could very kindly lean against me, 'cos I keep pulling so hard that I fall over backwards."

"Going on an Expotition?" said Pooh eagerly. "I don't think I've ever been on one of those. Where are we going to on this Expotition?"

"Expedition, silly old Bear. It's got an 'x' in it."

"What *is* the North Pole?" he asked.
"It's just a thing you discover," said Christopher Robin
carelessly, not being quite sure himself.

"That's what an
Expedition means.
A long line of
everybody . . .
And we must all
bring Provisions."
"Bring what?"
"Things to eat."

The Piglet was sitting on the ground at the door of his house blowing happily at a dandelion, and wondering whether it would be this year, next year, sometime, or never. He had just discovered that it would be never, and was trying to remember what '*it*' was, and hoping it wasn't anything nice, when Pooh came up.

"Oh! Piglet," said Pooh excitedly, "we're going on an Expotition, all of us, with things to eat . . ."

First came Christopher Robin and Rabbit, then Piglet and Pooh; then Kanga, with Roo in her pocket, and Owl; then Eeyore; and, at the end, in a long line, all Rabbit's friends-and-relations.

They all went off to discover the Pole,
    Owl and Piglet and Rabbit and all;
It's a Thing you Discover, as I've been tole
    by Owl and Piglet and Rabbit and all.
Eeyore, Christopher Robin and Pooh
And Rabbit's relations all went too –
And where the Pole was none of them knew . . .
    Sing Hey! for Owl and Rabbit and all!

"Hush!" said Christopher Robin, turning round to Pooh,
"we're just coming to a Dangerous Place."

"Hush!" they said hastily to each other all down the line, until it got to the last one of all. And the last and smallest friend-and-relation was so upset to find that the whole Expotition was saying "Hush!" to *him*, that he buried himself head downwards in a crack in the ground, and stayed there for two days until the danger was over, and then went home in a great hurry, and lived quietly with his Aunt ever-afterwards. His name was Alexander Beetle.

"An Ambush," said Owl, "is a sort of Surprise."

"So is a gorse-bush sometimes," said Pooh.

"I think," said Christopher Robin, "that we ought to eat all our Provisions now, so that we shan't have so much to carry."

"Eat all our what?" said Pooh.

"All that we've brought," said Piglet, getting to work.

Roo was washing his
face and paws in
the stream, while
Kanga explained
to everybody
proudly that this
was the first time
he had ever washed
his face himself . . .

"I don't hold with all this washing," grumbled Eeyore. "This modern Behind-the-ears nonsense. What do *you* think, Pooh?"

"So much for *washing*," said Eeyore.

"Roo's fallen in!" cried Rabbit, and he and Christopher Robin came rushing down to the rescue.

"Look at me swimming!" squeaked Roo from the middle of his pool, and was hurried down a waterfall into the next pool.

But Pooh . . . was standing with a long pole in his paws, and Kanga came up and took one end of it, and between them they held it across the lower part of the pool; and Roo, still bubbling proudly, "Look at me swimming," drifted up against it, and climbed out.

"Pooh," he said, "where did you find that pole?"
Pooh looked at the pole in his hands.
"I just found it," he said. "I thought it ought to be useful. I just picked it up."

"Pooh," said Christopher Robin solemnly, "the Expedition is over. You have found the North Pole!"

They stuck the pole in the ground, and Christopher Robin tied a message on to it:

NORTH POLE
DICSovERED By
POOH
POOH FoUND IT

Then they all went home again.
And I think, but I am not quite sure,
that Roo had a hot bath and went
straight to bed. But Pooh went back
to his own house, and feeling very
proud of what he had done, had a
little something to revive himself.